A Fearless Woman

2016 Date Book

january

She's become the one she imagined she could be

No surprise to those who know her,
she lives with a mission
to follow her true path.

Believing big, trusting her heart
and risking all, she creates the life
she imagines.

believing big

january

sun	mon	tues	wed	thur	fri	sat
					1	2
Flower: Carnation Gemstone: Garnet	Financial Wellness Month International Creativity Month				New Year's Day	Last Quarter Moon ◑
3	4	5	6	7	8	9
		Twelfth Night		Eastern Orthodox Christmas		
10	11	12	13	14	15	16
New Moon ●				Eastern Orthodox New Year		First Quarter Moon ◑
17	18	19	20	21	22	23
	Martin Luther King, Jr. Day					
24	25	26	27	28	29	30
Full Moon ○		Australia Day (AUS)				
31						

Notes

JANUARY

s	m	t	w	t	f	s
					1	2
3	4	5	6	7	8	9
10	11	12	13	14	15	16
17	18	19	20	21	22	23
24	25	26	27	28	29	30
31						

january

Notes

_____
_____
_____
_____
_____
_____
_____
_____
_____
_____
_____
_____
_____
_____

Flower: Carnation • Gemstone: Garnet • Financial Wellness Month • International Creativity Month

1 FRIDAY

New Year's Day

2 SATURDAY

Last Quarter Moon ☽

3 SUNDAY

Brush Dance

january

FEBRUARY

s	m	t	w	t	f	s
	1	2	3	4	5	6
7	8	9	10	11	12	13
14	15	16	17	18	19	20
21	22	23	24	25	26	27
28	29					

MONDAY 4

TUESDAY 5

Twelfth Night

WEDNESDAY 6

THURSDAY 7

Eastern Orthodox Christmas

FRIDAY 8

SATURDAY 9

SUNDAY 10

Brush Dance

New Moon ●

JANUARY

s	m	t	w	t	f	s
					1	2
3	4	5	6	7	8	9
10	11	12	13	14	15	16
17	18	19	20	21	22	23
24	25	26	27	28	29	30
31						

january

11 MONDAY

12 TUESDAY

13 WEDNESDAY

14 THURSDAY

Eastern Orthodox New Year

15 FRIDAY

16 SATURDAY

First Quarter Moon ☽

17 SUNDAY

january

FEBRUARY

s	m	t	w	t	f	s
	1	2	3	4	5	6
7	8	9	10	11	12	13
14	15	16	17	18	19	20
21	22	23	24	25	26	27
28	29					

MONDAY 18

TUESDAY 19

Martin Luther King, Jr. Day

WEDNESDAY 20

THURSDAY 21

FRIDAY 22

SATURDAY 23

SUNDAY 24

Brush Dance

Full Moon ○

JANUARY

s	m	t	w	t	f	s
					1	2
3	4	5	6	7	8	9
10	11	12	13	14	15	16
17	18	19	20	21	22	23
24	25	26	27	28	29	30
31						

january

25 MONDAY

26 TUESDAY

Australia Day (AUS)

27 WEDNESDAY

28 THURSDAY

29 FRIDAY

30 SATURDAY

31 SUNDAY

Brush Dance

Notes

Notes

Notes

passion flower

She blooms with power and purpose

february

Imagine your passion as a radiant flower, a vivid blend of power and purpose.

It's your soul's very essence blooming inside, uplifting you and guiding you.

february

sun	mon	tues	wed	thur	fri	sat
	1	2	3	4	5	6
Flower: Violet Gemstone: Amethyst	National Freedom Day Last Quarter Moon ◑	Groundhog Day			Constitution Day (MEX)	Waitangi Day (NZ)
7	8	9	10	11	12	13
	Chinese New Year (Year of the Monkey) New Moon ●	Mardi Gras	Ash Wednesday		Lincoln's Birthday	
14	15	16	17	18	19	20
Valentine's Day	Susan B. Anthony Day Nirvana Day President's Day Washington's Birthday First Quarter Moon ◐					
21	22	23	24	25	26	27
	Full Moon ○					
28	29					Black History Month National Mend a Broken Heart Month

Notes

FEBRUARY

s	m	t	w	t	f	s
	1	2	3	4	5	6
7	8	9	10	11	12	13
14	15	16	17	18	19	20
21	22	23	24	25	26	27
28	29					

february

Flower: Violet • Gemstone: Amethyst • Black History Month • National Mend a Broken Heart Month

1 MONDAY

National Freedom Day
Last Quarter Moon ☽

2 TUESDAY

Groundhog Day

3 WEDNESDAY

4 THURSDAY

5 FRIDAY

Constitution Day (MEX)

6 SATURDAY

Waitangi Day (NZ)

7 SUNDAY

Brush Dance

february

MARCH

s	m	t	w	t	f	s
		1	2	3	4	5
6	7	8	9	10	11	12
13	14	15	16	17	18	19
20	21	22	23	24	25	26
27	28	29	30	31		

MONDAY 8

Chinese New Year (Year of the Monkey)
New Moon ●

TUESDAY 9

Mardi Gras

WEDNESDAY 10

Ash Wednesday

THURSDAY 11

FRIDAY 12

Lincoln's Birthday

SATURDAY 13

SUNDAY 14

Brush Dance

Valentine's Day

FEBRUARY

s	m	t	w	t	f	s
	1	2	3	4	5	6
7	8	9	10	11	12	13
14	15	16	17	18	19	20
21	22	23	24	25	26	27
28	29					

february

15 MONDAY

16 TUESDAY

Susan B. Anthony Day
Nirvana Day
President's Day
Washington's Birthday
First Quarter Moon ☽

17 WEDNESDAY

18 THURSDAY

19 FRIDAY

20 SATURDAY

21 SUNDAY

Brush Dance

february

MARCH

s	m	t	w	t	f	s
		1	2	3	4	5
6	7	8	9	10	11	12
13	14	15	16	17	18	19
20	21	22	23	24	25	26
27	28	29	30	31		

MONDAY 22

TUESDAY 23

Full Moon ○

WEDNESDAY 24

THURSDAY 25

FRIDAY 26

SATURDAY 27

SUNDAY 28

Brush Dance

FEBRUARY

s	m	t	w	t	f	s
	1	2	3	4	5	6
7	8	9	10	11	12	13
14	15	16	17	18	19	20
21	22	23	24	25	26	27
28	29					

february

29 MONDAY

I TUESDAY

Notes

Notes

Notes

Notes

we are
fearless
women

We are fierce with our feminine
power. We are beautiful and bold,
audacious and courageous.

Wise and creative, gutsy and strong,
we will not be silenced or ignored.

We bravely walk on to any stage,
open-heartedly speaking the truth,
making no excuses whatsoever
for who we are, for how we live,
for what we believe.

We are fearless women, beautiful
and bold, unstoppable, indomitable.

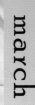

march

no excuses whatsoever no excuses whatsoever no excuses

march

sun	mon	tues	wed	thur	fri	sat
		1 Last Quarter Moon ◑	2	3 National Anthem Day	4	5
Flower: Daffodil Gemstone: Aquamarine						
6 Mothering Sunday (UK)	7	8 International Women's Day	9 New Moon ●	10	11	12 Plant a Flower Day
13 Daylight Saving Time begins (US & CAN)	14 Commonwealth Day (CAN & UK)	15 First Quarter Moon ◑	16	17 St. Patrick's Day	18	19
20 Vernal Equinox - Spring begins Palm Sunday	21 Benito Juárez Birthday (MEX)	22	23 Full Moon ○	24 Purim	25 Good Friday	26
27 Easter British Summer Time begins (UK)	28 Easter Monday	29	30	31 César Chávez Day Last Quarter Moon ◑		Women's History Month National Nutrition Month

Notes

MARCH

s	m	t	w	t	f	s
		1	2	3	4	5
6	7	8	9	10	11	12
13	14	15	16	17	18	19
20	21	22	23	24	25	26
27	28	29	30	31		

march

Flower: Daffodil • Gemstone: Aquamarine • Women's History Month • National Nutrition Month

29 MONDAY

1 TUESDAY

Last Quarter Moon ◑

2 WEDNESDAY

3 THURSDAY

National Anthem Day

4 FRIDAY

5 SATURDAY

6 SUNDAY

Mothering Sunday (UK)

Brush Dance

march

APRIL

s	m	t	w	t	f	s
					1	2
3	4	5	6	7	8	9
10	11	12	13	14	15	16
17	18	19	20	21	22	23
24	25	26	27	28	29	30

MONDAY 7

TUESDAY 8

International Women's Day

WEDNESDAY 9

THURSDAY 10

New Moon ●

FRIDAY 11

SATURDAY 12

Plant a Flower Day

SUNDAY 13

Brush Dance

Daylight Saving Time begins (US & CAN)

MARCH

s	m	t	w	t	f	s
		1	2	3	4	5
6	7	8	9	10	11	12
13	14	15	16	17	18	19
20	21	22	23	24	25	26
27	28	29	30	31		

march

14 MONDAY

Commonwealth Day (CAN & UK)

15 TUESDAY

First Quarter Moon ◑

16 WEDNESDAY

17 THURSDAY

St. Patrick's Day

18 FRIDAY

19 SATURDAY

20 SUNDAY

Vernal Equinox - Spring begins
Palm Sunday

Brush Dance

march

APRIL

s	m	t	w	t	f	s
					1	2
3	4	5	6	7	8	9
10	11	12	13	14	15	16
17	18	19	20	21	22	23
24	25	26	27	28	29	30

MONDAY 21

Benito Juárez Birthday (MEX)

TUESDAY 22

WEDNESDAY 23

Full Moon ○

THURSDAY 24

Purim

FRIDAY 25

Good Friday

SATURDAY 26

SUNDAY 27

Easter
British Summer Time begins (UK)

Brush Dance

MARCH

s	m	t	w	t	f	s
		1	2	3	4	5
6	7	8	9	10	11	12
13	14	15	16	17	18	19
20	21	22	23	24	25	26
27	28	29	30	31		

march

28 MONDAY

Easter Monday

29 TUESDAY

30 WEDNESDAY

31 THURSDAY

César Chávez Day
Last Quarter Moon ◑

Notes

_____

_____

_____

_____

_____

_____

_____

_____

_____

_____

_____

Notes

Notes

Notes

She surrenders her fear

Isn't this really the test
of all tests? To let go
of your fear even when
you feel the worst
you could feel.

As you surrender your fear
you're lifted aloft toward
renewal, even revelation.
Angel wings seem to catch you.

Letting go of your fear opens
up a rare opportunity to
reignite your purpose and,
maybe, truly know yourself
for the first time.

letting go

april

sun	mon	tues	wed	thur	fri	sat
					1 April Fool's Day	2 International Children's Book Day
Flower: Daisy Gemstone: Diamond	National Garden Month Celebrate Diversity Month					
3	4	5	6	7 World Health Day New Moon ●	8	9
10	11	12	13	14 First Quarter Moon ◐	15	16
17	18	19	20 Volunteer Recognition Day	21	22 Earth Day Full Moon ○	23 Passover
24	25 ANZAC Day (AUS & NZ)	26	27 Administrative Professionals Day	28	29 Arbor Day	30 Día de los Niños Last Quarter Moon ◑

Notes

_____

_____

_____

APRIL

s	m	t	w	t	f	s
					1	2
3	4	5	6	7	8	9
10	11	12	13	14	15	16
17	18	19	20	21	22	23
24	25	26	27	28	29	30

april

Notes

Flower: Daisy • Gemstone: Diamond • National Garden Month • Celebrate Diversity Month

1 FRIDAY

2 SATURDAY

April Fool's Day

International Children's Book Day

3 SUNDAY

Brush Dance

april

MAY

s	m	t	w	t	f	s
1	2	3	4	5	6	7
8	9	10	11	12	13	14
15	16	17	18	19	20	21
22	23	24	25	26	27	28
29	30	31				

MONDAY 4

TUESDAY 5

WEDNESDAY 6

THURSDAY 7

World Health Day
New Moon ●

FRIDAY 8

SATURDAY 9

SUNDAY 10

Brush Dance

APRIL

s	m	t	w	t	f	s
					1	2
3	4	5	6	7	8	9
10	11	12	13	14	15	16
17	18	19	20	21	22	23
24	25	26	27	28	29	30

april

11 MONDAY

12 TUESDAY

13 WEDNESDAY

14 THURSDAY

First Quarter Moon ◗

15 FRIDAY

16 SATURDAY

17 SUNDAY

Brush Dance

april

MAY

s	m	t	w	t	f	s
1	2	3	4	5	6	7
8	9	10	11	12	13	14
15	16	17	18	19	20	21
22	23	24	25	26	27	28
29	30	31				

MONDAY 18

TUESDAY 19

WEDNESDAY 20

THURSDAY 21

Volunteer Recognition Day

FRIDAY 22

SATURDAY 23

Earth Day
Full Moon ○

Passover

SUNDAY 24

Brush Dance

APRIL

s	m	t	w	t	f	s
					1	2
3	4	5	6	7	8	9
10	11	12	13	14	15	16
17	18	19	20	21	22	23
24	25	26	27	28	29	30

april

25 MONDAY

26 TUESDAY

ANZAC Day (AUS & NZ)

27 WEDNESDAY

28 THURSDAY

Administrative Professionals Day

29 FRIDAY

30 SATURDAY

Arbor Day

Día de los Niños
Last Quarter Moon ◑

Notes

Brush Dance

Notes

Notes

Notes

shining through

How often do you fall into the silly habit of catching yourself being unworthy or foolish?

What if you were to suddenly shift from foolish to fearless? Yes, you can do this! Easy as pride.

You can catch yourself flourishing, flowering and flowing, being free.

You can catch your fearless spirit shining through.

may

sun	mon	tues	wed	thur	fri	sat
1 May Day Labor Day (MEX)	2 Early May Bank Holiday (UK)	3 National Teacher Day	4	5 Cinco de Mayo (MEX) National Day of Prayer Ascension Day	6 New Moon ●	7
8 Mother's Day	9	10	11	12	13 First Quarter Moon ◐	14
15 International Day of Families	16	17	18	19	20	21 Armed Forces Day Full Moon ○
22	23 Victoria Day (CAN)	24	25	26	27	28
29 Last Quarter Moon ◑	30 Spring Bank Holiday (UK) Memorial Day	31			Flower: Lily of the Valley Gemstone: Emerald	Older Americans Month National Meditation Month

Notes

MAY

s	m	t	w	t	f	s
1	2	3	4	5	6	7
8	9	10	11	12	13	14
15	16	17	18	19	20	21
22	23	24	25	26	27	28
29	30	31				

may

Notes

Flower: Lily of the Valley • Gemstone: Emerald • Older Americans Month • National Meditation Month

I SUNDAY

May Day
Labor Day (MEX)

Brush Dance

may

JUNE

s	m	t	w	t	f	s
			1	2	3	4
5	6	7	8	9	10	11
12	13	14	15	16	17	18
19	20	21	22	23	24	25
26	27	28	29	30		

MONDAY 2

Early May Bank Holiday (UK)

TUESDAY 3

National Teacher Day

WEDNESDAY 4

THURSDAY 5

Cinco de Mayo (MEX)
National Day of Prayer
Ascension Day

FRIDAY 6

New Moon ●

SATURDAY 7

SUNDAY 8

Brush Dance

Mother's Day

MAY

s	m	t	w	t	f	s
1	2	3	4	5	6	7
8	9	10	11	12	13	14
15	16	17	18	19	20	21
22	23	24	25	26	27	28
29	30	31				

may

9 MONDAY

10 TUESDAY

11 WEDNESDAY

12 THURSDAY

13 FRIDAY

14 SATURDAY

First Quarter Moon ☽

15 SUNDAY

International Day of Families

Brush Dance

may

JUNE

s	m	t	w	t	f	s
			1	2	3	4
5	6	7	8	9	10	11
12	13	14	15	16	17	18
19	20	21	22	23	24	25
26	27	28	29	30		

MONDAY 16

TUESDAY 17

WEDNESDAY 18

THURSDAY 19

FRIDAY 20

SATURDAY 21

Armed Forces Day
Full Moon ○

SUNDAY 22

Brush Dance

MAY

s	m	t	w	t	f	s
1	2	3	4	5	6	7
8	9	10	11	12	13	14
15	16	17	18	19	20	21
22	23	24	25	26	27	28
29	30	31				

may

23 MONDAY

24 TUESDAY

Victoria Day (CAN)

25 WEDNESDAY

26 THURSDAY

27 FRIDAY

28 SATURDAY

29 SUNDAY

Last Quarter Moon ◐

Brush Dance

may

JUNE

s	m	t	w	t	f	s
			1	2	3	4
5	6	7	8	9	10	11
12	13	14	15	16	17	18
19	20	21	22	23	24	25
26	27	28	29	30		

MONDAY 30

TUESDAY 31

Spring Bank Holiday (UK)

Memorial Day

Notes

Notes

Notes

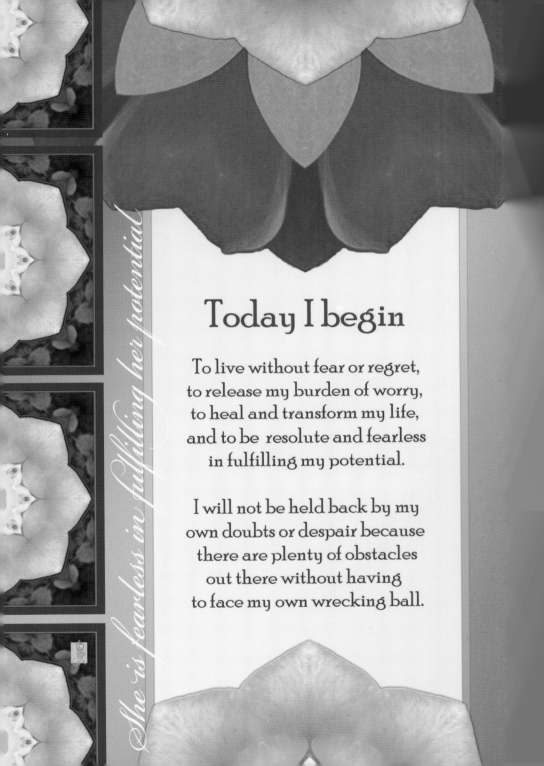

Today I begin

To live without fear or regret,
to release my burden of worry,
to heal and transform my life,
and to be resolute and fearless
in fulfilling my potential.

I will not be held back by my
own doubts or despair because
there are plenty of obstacles
out there without having
to face my own wrecking ball.

She is fearless in fulfilling her potential

june

sun	mon	tues	wed	thur	fri	sat
			1	2	3	4
Flower: Rose Gemstone: Alexandrite			Go Barefoot Day			
5	6	7	8	9	10	11
World Environment Day New Moon ●	Queen's Birthday (NZ) Ramadan begins		Best Friends Day			
12	13	14	15	16	17	18
First Quarter Moon ◐	Queen's Birthday (AUS)	Flag Day			Eat Your Vegetables Day	
19	20	21	22	23	24	25
Father's Day	Summer Solstice - Summer begins Full Moon ○	World Music Day				
26	27	28	29	30		
	Last Quarter Moon ◑					National Iced Tea Month Children's Awareness Month

Notes

JUNE

s	m	t	w	t	f	s
			1	2	3	4
5	6	7	8	9	10	11
12	13	14	15	16	17	18
19	20	21	22	23	24	25
26	27	28	29	30		

june

Notes

Flower: Rose • Gemstone: Alexandrite • National Iced Tea Month • Children's Awareness Month

1 WEDNESDAY

2 THURSDAY

Go Barefoot Day

3 FRIDAY

4 SATURDAY

5 SUNDAY

World Environment Day
New Moon ●

Brush Dance

june

JULY

s	m	t	w	t	f	s
					1	2
3	4	5	6	7	8	9
10	11	12	13	14	15	16
17	18	19	20	21	22	23
24	25	26	27	28	29	30
31						

MONDAY 6

TUESDAY 7

Queen's Birthday (NZ)
Ramadan begins

WEDNESDAY 8

THURSDAY 9

Best Friends Day

FRIDAY 10

SATURDAY 11

SUNDAY 12

Brush Dance

First Quarter Moon ◑

JUNE

s	m	t	w	t	f	s
			1	2	3	4
5	6	7	8	9	10	11
12	13	14	15	16	17	18
19	20	21	22	23	24	25
26	27	28	29	30		

june

13 MONDAY

Queen's Birthday (AUS)

14 TUESDAY

Flag Day

15 WEDNESDAY

16 THURSDAY

17 FRIDAY

Eat Your Vegetables Day

18 SATURDAY

19 SUNDAY

Father's Day

Brush Dance

june

JULY

s	m	t	w	t	f	s
					1	2
3	4	5	6	7	8	9
10	11	12	13	14	15	16
17	18	19	20	21	22	23
24	25	26	27	28	29	30
31						

MONDAY **20**

Summer Solstice - Summer begins
Full Moon ○

TUESDAY **21**

World Music Day

WEDNESDAY **22**

THURSDAY **23**

FRIDAY **24**

SATURDAY **25**

SUNDAY **26**

Brush Dance

JUNE

s	m	t	w	t	f	s
			1	2	3	4
5	6	7	8	9	10	11
12	13	14	15	16	17	18
19	20	21	22	23	24	25
26	27	28	29	30		

june

27 MONDAY

28 TUESDAY

Last Quarter Moon ◑

29 WEDNESDAY

30 THURSDAY

Notes

_____

_____

_____

_____

_____

_____

_____

_____

_____

Notes

Notes

Notes

acallingastirringaheart-feltfantasy

it's never too late

How long has it been since you used your voice, shared your gifts, felt your passion?

How long since you've taken a risk or attempted a leap?

How long since you've acted on a heart-felt fantasy or a deep stirring?

It's never too late to begin what intrigues you, what calls you or stirs you.

It's never too late.

She feels a deep stirring

july

sun	mon	tues	wed	thur	fri	sat
					1	2
	National Ice Cream Month / Sarcoma Awareness Month					
Flower: Larkspur / Gemstone: Ruby					Canada Day	
3	4	5	6	7	8	9
	Independence Day / New Moon ●	Eid al-Fitr (Ramadan ends)				
10	11	12	13	14	15	16
		First Quarter Moon ◑				
17	18	19	20	21	22	23
		Full Moon ○				
24	25	26	27	28	29	30
Cousins' Day / Parents' Day						
31		Last Quarter Moon ◐				

Notes

JULY

s	m	t	w	t	f	s
					1	2
3	4	5	6	7	8	9
10	11	12	13	14	15	16
17	18	19	20	21	22	23
24	25	26	27	28	29	30
31						

july

Notes

_____
_____
_____
_____
_____
_____
_____
_____
_____
_____
_____
_____
_____
_____
_____
_____

Flower: Larkspur • Gemstone: Ruby • National Ice Cream Month • Sarcoma Awareness Month

1 FRIDAY

2 SATURDAY

Canada Day

3 SUNDAY

Brush Dance

july

AUGUST

s	m	t	w	t	f	s
	1	2	3	4	5	6
7	8	9	10	11	12	13
14	15	16	17	18	19	20
21	22	23	24	25	26	27
28	29	30	31			

MONDAY **4**

Independence Day
New Moon ●

TUESDAY **5**

Eid al-Fitr (Ramadan ends)

WEDNESDAY **6**

THURSDAY **7**

FRIDAY **8**

SATURDAY **9**

SUNDAY **10**

Brush Dance

JULY

s	m	t	w	t	f	s
					1	2
3	4	5	6	7	8	9
10	11	12	13	14	15	16
17	18	19	20	21	22	23
24	25	26	27	28	29	30
31						

july

11 MONDAY

12 TUESDAY

First Quarter Moon ☽

13 WEDNESDAY

14 THURSDAY

15 FRIDAY

16 SATURDAY

17 SUNDAY

Brush Dance

july

AUGUST

s	m	t	w	t	f	s
	1	2	3	4	5	6
7	8	9	10	11	12	13
14	15	16	17	18	19	20
21	22	23	24	25	26	27
28	29	30	31			

MONDAY 18

TUESDAY 19

Full Moon ○

WEDNESDAY 20

THURSDAY 21

FRIDAY 22

SATURDAY 23

SUNDAY 24

Brush Dance

Cousins' Day
Parents' Day

JULY

s	m	t	w	t	f	s
					1	2
3	4	5	6	7	8	9
10	11	12	13	14	15	16
17	18	19	20	21	22	23
24	25	26	27	28	29	30
31						

july

25 MONDAY

26 TUESDAY

Last Quarter Moon ◑

27 WEDNESDAY

28 THURSDAY

29 FRIDAY

30 SATURDAY

31 SUNDAY

Brush Dance

Notes

Notes

Notes

medicine for the soul

Following the Fearless Way
is medicine for the soul, healing
and transforming the past, focusing
your heart in the present, creating
a path to future potential.

If your soul feels adrift,
try a spoonful of Fearless!

It soothes the fever of fear,
restoring you to wholeness,
renewing your vitality.

*She is transformed
and renewed*

august

sun	mon	tues	wed	thur	fri	sat
	1 Civic Holiday (CAN) Summer Bank Holiday (SCT)	2 New Moon ●	3 National Watermelon Day	4	5	6
7 Friendship Day National Lighthouse Day	8	9	10 First Quarter Moon ◑	11	12 International Youth Day	13 Left Handers Day
14	15	16	17	18 Full Moon ○	19 National Aviation Day	20
21	22	23	24	25 Kiss & Make Up Day Last Quarter Moon ◐	26 Women's Equality Day	27 Global Forgiveness Day
28	29 Summer Bank Holiday (UK)	30	31		Flower: Gladiolus Gemstone: Peridot	Romance Awareness Month Happiness Happens Month

Notes

AUGUST

s	m	t	w	t	f	s
	1	2	3	4	5	6
7	8	9	10	11	12	13
14	15	16	17	18	19	20
21	22	23	24	25	26	27
28	29	30	31			

august

Flower: Gladiolus • Gemstone: Peridot • Romance Awareness Month • Happiness Happens Month

1 MONDAY

Civic Holiday (CAN)
Summer Bank Holiday (SCT)

2 TUESDAY

New Moon ●

3 WEDNESDAY

National Watermelon Day

4 THURSDAY

5 FRIDAY

6 SATURDAY

7 SUNDAY

Friendship Day
National Lighthouse Day

Brush Dance

august

SEPTEMBER

s	m	t	w	t	f	s
					1	2	3
4	5	6	7	8	9	10
11	12	13	14	15	16	17
18	19	20	21	22	23	24
25	26	27	28	29	30	

MONDAY 8

TUESDAY 9

WEDNESDAY 10

THURSDAY 11

First Quarter Moon ◐

FRIDAY 12

SATURDAY 13

International Youth Day

Left Handers Day

SUNDAY 14

Brush Dance

AUGUST

s	m	t	w	t	f	s
	1	2	3	4	5	6
7	8	9	10	11	12	13
14	15	16	17	18	19	20
21	22	23	24	25	26	27
28	29	30	31			

15 MONDAY

16 TUESDAY

17 WEDNESDAY

18 THURSDAY

Full Moon ○

19 FRIDAY

20 SATURDAY

National Aviation Day

21 SUNDAY

Brush Dance

august

SEPTEMBER

s	m	t	w	t	f	s
				1	2	3
4	5	6	7	8	9	10
11	12	13	14	15	16	17
18	19	20	21	22	23	24
25	26	27	28	29	30	

MONDAY 22

TUESDAY 23

WEDNESDAY 24

THURSDAY 25

Kiss & Make Up Day
Last Quarter Moon ◗

FRIDAY 26

SATURDAY 27

Women's Equality Day

Global Forgiveness Day

SUNDAY 28

Brush Dance

AUGUST

s	m	t	w	t	f	s
	1	2	3	4	5	6
7	8	9	10	11	12	13
14	15	16	17	18	19	20
21	22	23	24	25	26	27
28	29	30	31			

august

29 MONDAY

30 TUESDAY

Summer Bank Holiday (UK)

31 WEDNESDAY

I THURSDAY

Notes

Brush Dance

Notes

Notes

Notes

Brush Dance

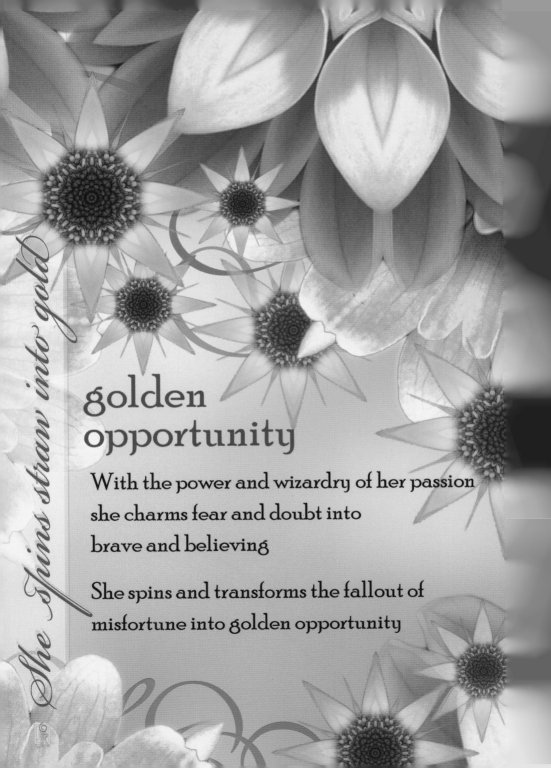

She Spins straw into gold

golden opportunity

With the power and wizardry of her passion
she charms fear and doubt into
brave and believing

She spins and transforms the fallout of
misfortune into golden opportunity

september

sun	mon	tues	wed	thur	fri	sat
				1	2	3
Flower: Aster Gemstone: Sapphire				New Moon ●		
4	5	6	7	8	9	10
	Labor Day (US & CAN)				First Quarter Moon ◑	
11	12	13	14	15	16	17
Grandparents Day Eid al-Adha (Islamic Feast of Sacrifice)					Independence Day (MEX) Full Moon ○	Citizenship Day
18	19	20	21	22	23	24
			World Gratitude Day International Day of Peace	Autumnal Equinox - Fall begins	Native American Day Last Quarter Moon ◐	
25	26	27	28	29	30	
	Johnny Appleseed Day					Ovarian Cancer Awareness Month Self Improvement Month

Notes

SEPTEMBER

s	m	t	w	t	f	s
				1	2	3
4	5	6	7	8	9	10
11	12	13	14	15	16	17
18	19	20	21	22	23	24
25	26	27	28	29	30	

september

Notes

Flower: Aster • Gemstone: Sapphire • Ovarian Cancer Awareness Month • Self Improvement Month

31 WEDNESDAY

1 THURSDAY

New Moon ●

2 FRIDAY

3 SATURDAY

4 SUNDAY

Brush Dance

september

OCTOBER

s	m	t	w	t	f	s
						1
2	3	4	5	6	7	8
9	10	11	12	13	14	15
16	17	18	19	20	21	22
23	24	25	26	27	28	29
30	31					

MONDAY 5

TUESDAY 6

Labor Day (US & CAN)

WEDNESDAY 7

THURSDAY 8

FRIDAY 9

SATURDAY 10

First Quarter Moon ☽

SUNDAY 11

Grandparents Day

Eid al-Adha (Islamic Feast of Sacrifice)

Brush Dance

SEPTEMBER

s	m	t	w	t	f	s
				1	2	3
4	5	6	7	8	9	10
11	12	13	14	15	16	17
18	19	20	21	22	23	24
25	26	27	28	29	30	

september

12 MONDAY

13 TUESDAY

14 WEDNESDAY

15 THURSDAY

16 FRIDAY

17 SATURDAY

Independence Day (MEX)
Full Moon ○

Citizenship Day

18 SUNDAY

Brush Dance

september

OCTOBER

s	m	t	w	t	f	s
						1
2	3	4	5	6	7	8
9	10	11	12	13	14	15
16	17	18	19	20	21	22
23	24	25	26	27	28	29
30	31					

MONDAY 19

TUESDAY 20

WEDNESDAY 21

THURSDAY 22

World Gratitude Day
International Day of Peace

Autumnal Equinox - Fall begins

FRIDAY 23

SATURDAY 24

Native American Day
Last Quarter Moon ◑

SUNDAY 25

Brush Dance

SEPTEMBER

s	m	t	w	t	f	s
				1	2	3
4	5	6	7	8	9	10
11	12	13	14	15	16	17
18	19	20	21	22	23	24
25	26	27	28	29	30	

september

26 MONDAY

27 TUESDAY

Johnny Appleseed Day

28 WEDNESDAY

29 THURSDAY

30 FRIDAY

I SATURDAY

Notes

Notes

Notes

Notes

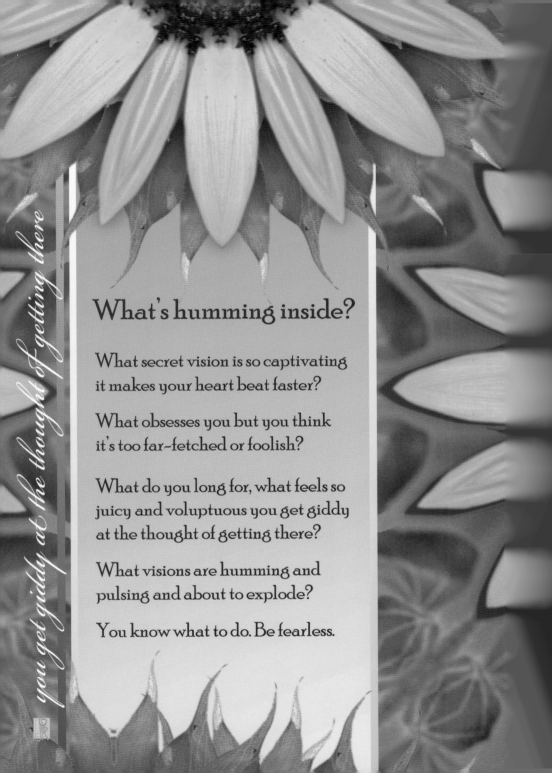

What's humming inside?

What secret vision is so captivating
it makes your heart beat faster?

What obsesses you but you think
it's too far-fetched or foolish?

What do you long for, what feels so
juicy and voluptuous you get giddy
at the thought of getting there?

What visions are humming and
pulsing and about to explode?

You know what to do. Be fearless.

you get giddy at the thought of getting there

october

sun	mon	tues	wed	thur	fri	sat
						1 New Moon ●
Flower: Cosmos Gemstone: Opal	Breast Cancer Awareness Month					
2 al-Hijra (Islamic New Year)	**3** Rosh Hashanah	**4**	**5**	**6**	**7**	**8**
9 First Quarter Moon ☽	**10** Thanksgiving (CAN) Columbus Day	**11**	**12** Yom Kippur	**13**	**14**	**15**
16 Full Moon ○	**17** Boss's Day	**18**	**19**	**20**	**21**	**22** Last Quarter Moon ☽
23	**24** United Nations Day Labour Day (NZ)	**25**	**26**	**27**	**28**	**29**
30 British Summer Time ends (UK) New Moon ●	**31** Halloween					

Notes

_____

_____

_____

OCTOBER

s	m	t	w	t	f	s
						1
2	3	4	5	6	7	8
9	10	11	12	13	14	15
16	17	18	19	20	21	22
23	24	25	26	27	28	29
30	31					

october

Notes

Flower: Cosmos • Gemstone: Opal • Breast Cancer Awareness Month

30 FRIDAY

Time to Order Your
2017 Calendars
at www.brushdance.com

1 SATURDAY

New Moon ●

2 SUNDAY

al-Hijra (Islamic New Year)

Brush Dance

october

NOVEMBER

s	m	t	w	t	f	s
		1	2	3	4	5
6	7	8	9	10	11	12
13	14	15	16	17	18	19
20	21	22	23	24	25	26
27	28	29	30			

MONDAY 3

TUESDAY 4

Rosh Hashanah

WEDNESDAY 5

THURSDAY 6

FRIDAY 7

SATURDAY 8

SUNDAY 9

Brush Dance

First Quarter Moon ◗

OCTOBER

s	m	t	w	t	f	s
						1
2	3	4	5	6	7	8
9	10	11	12	13	14	15
16	17	18	19	20	21	22
23	24	25	26	27	28	29
30	31					

october

IO MONDAY

Thanksgiving (CAN)
Columbus Day

II TUESDAY

I2 WEDNESDAY

Yom Kippur

I3 THURSDAY

I4 FRIDAY

I5 SATURDAY

I6 SUNDAY

Full Moon ○

Brush Dance

october

NOVEMBER

s	m	t	w	t	f	s
		1	2	3	4	5
6	7	8	9	10	11	12
13	14	15	16	17	18	19
20	21	22	23	24	25	26
27	28	29	30			

MONDAY **17**

TUESDAY **18**

Boss's Day

WEDNESDAY **19**

THURSDAY **20**

FRIDAY **21**

SATURDAY **22**

Last Quarter Moon ☽

SUNDAY **23**

Brush Dance

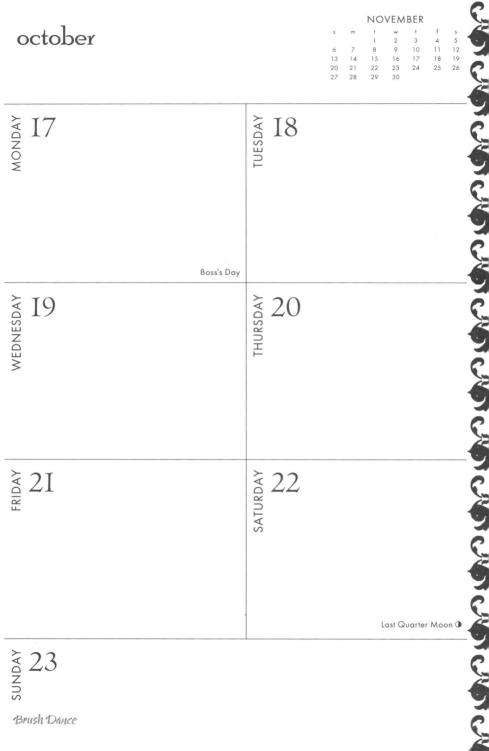

OCTOBER

s	m	t	w	t	f	s
						1
2	3	4	5	6	7	8
9	10	11	12	13	14	15
16	17	18	19	20	21	22
23	24	25	26	27	28	29
30	31					

october

24 MONDAY

25 TUESDAY

United Nations Day
Labour Day (NZ)

26 WEDNESDAY

27 THURSDAY

28 FRIDAY

29 SATURDAY

30 SUNDAY

British Summer Time ends (UK)
New Moon ●

Brush Dance

october

NOVEMBER

s	m	t	w	t	f	s
		1	2	3	4	5
6	7	8	9	10	11	12
13	14	15	16	17	18	19
20	21	22	23	24	25	26
27	28	29	30			

MONDAY 31

TUESDAY 1

Halloween

Notes

Brush Dance

Notes

Notes

imagine
your vision

living from the bigger part of your heart

What do you picture in your mind?

What is your outlook, your attitude, your vision?

Do you see through a lens of limitation or a lens of
mystery and possibility? Are you living from
the small worries of your mind or
from the bigger part of your heart ?

november

sun	mon	tues	wed	thur	fri	sat
		1	2	3	4	5
Flower: Chrysanthemum Gemstone: Topaz		All Saints' Day Día de los Muertos	All Souls' Day		Fountain Pen Day	
6	7	8	9	10	11	12
Daylight Saving Time ends (US & CAN)	First Quarter Moon ☽	Election Day (US)			Veterans Day Remembrance Day (CAN)	
13	14	15	16	17	18	19
	Full Moon ○	America Recycles Day	International Day for Tolerance			
20	21	22	23	24	25	26
	Last Quarter Moon ☾			Thanksgiving		
27	28	29	30			American Diabetes Month Adoption Awareness Month
		New Moon ●				

Notes

NOVEMBER

s	m	t	w	t	f	s
		1	2	3	4	5
6	7	8	9	10	11	12
13	14	15	16	17	18	19
20	21	22	23	24	25	26
27	28	29	30			

november

Flower: Chrysanthemum • Gemstone: Topaz • American Diabetes Month • Adoption Awareness Month

31 MONDAY

1 TUESDAY

All Saints' Day
Día de los Muertos

2 WEDNESDAY

3 THURSDAY

All Souls' Day

4 FRIDAY

5 SATURDAY

Fountain Pen Day

6 SUNDAY

Daylight Saving Time ends (US & CAN)

Brush Dance

november

DECEMBER

s	m	t	w	t	f	s
					1	2	3
4	5	6	7	8	9	10
11	12	13	14	15	16	17
18	19	20	21	22	23	24
25	26	27	28	29	30	31

MONDAY 7

First Quarter Moon ☽

TUESDAY 8

Election Day (US)

WEDNESDAY 9

THURSDAY 10

FRIDAY 11

Veterans Day
Remembrance Day (CAN)

SATURDAY 12

SUNDAY 13

Brush Dance

NOVEMBER

s	m	t	w	t	f	s
		1	2	3	4	5
6	7	8	9	10	11	12
13	14	15	16	17	18	19
20	21	22	23	24	25	26
27	28	29	30			

november

14 MONDAY

Full Moon ○

15 TUESDAY

America Recycles Day

16 WEDNESDAY

International Day for Tolerance

17 THURSDAY

18 FRIDAY

19 SATURDAY

20 SUNDAY

Brush Dance

november

DECEMBER

s	m	t	w	t	f	s
					1	2	3
4	5	6	7	8	9	10
11	12	13	14	15	16	17
18	19	20	21	22	23	24
25	26	27	28	29	30	31

MONDAY 21

TUESDAY 22

Last Quarter Moon ◑

WEDNESDAY 23

THURSDAY 24

Thanksgiving

FRIDAY 25

SATURDAY 26

SUNDAY 27

Brush Dance

NOVEMBER

s	m	t	w	t	f	s
		1	2	3	4	5
6	7	8	9	10	11	12
13	14	15	16	17	18	19
20	21	22	23	24	25	26
27	28	29	30			

november

28 MONDAY

29 TUESDAY

New Moon ●

30 WEDNESDAY

I THURSDAY

Notes

_____

_____

_____

_____

_____

_____

_____

_____

_____

Brush Dance

Notes

Notes

Notes

kinship

She celebrates her kinship with all of life

In a circle of love, she finds comfort and connection even in the darkest night. In the embrace of kinship, she rediscovers her own worthiness, purpose and joy.

december

sun	mon	tues	wed	thur	fri	sat
				1 World AIDS Day	**2**	**3**
4 Flower: Narcissus Gemstone: Turquoise	**5** Write a Friend Month Spiritual Literacy Month	**6**	**7** Pearl Harbor Remembrance Day First Quarter Moon ◐	**8** Bodhi Day	**9**	**10** Human Rights Day
11 Mawlid al-Nabi (Muhammad's Birthday)	**12** Our Lady of Guadalupe Day (MEX)	**13**	**14** Full Moon ○	**15**	**16**	**17**
18	**19**	**20**	**21** Winter Solstice - Winter begins Last Quarter Moon ◑	**22**	**23**	**24** Christmas Eve
25 Hanukkah Christmas	**26** Kwanzaa begins St. Stephen's Day (IRE) Boxing Day (AUS, CAN, NZ, & UK)	**27**	**28**	**29** New Moon ●	**30**	**31** New Year's Eve

Notes

DECEMBER

s	m	t	w	t	f	s
				1	2	3
4	5	6	7	8	9	10
11	12	13	14	15	16	17
18	19	20	21	22	23	24
25	26	27	28	29	30	31

december

Notes

Flower: Narcissus • Gemstone: Turquoise • Write a Friend Month • Spiritual Literacy Month

30 WEDNESDAY

1 THURSDAY

World AIDS Day

2 FRIDAY

3 SATURDAY

4 SUNDAY

Brush Dance

december

JANUARY 2017

s	m	t	w	t	f	s
1	2	3	4	5	6	7
8	9	10	11	12	13	14
15	16	17	18	19	20	21
22	23	24	25	26	27	28
29	30	31				

MONDAY 5

TUESDAY 6

WEDNESDAY 7

THURSDAY 8

Pearl Harbor Remembrance Day
First Quarter Moon ☽

Bodhi Day

FRIDAY 9

SATURDAY 10

Human Rights Day

SUNDAY 11

Brush Dance

Mawlid al-Nabi (Muhammad's Birthday)

DECEMBER

s	m	t	w	t	f	s
				1	2	3
4	5	6	7	8	9	10
11	12	13	14	15	16	17
18	19	20	21	22	23	24
25	26	27	28	29	30	31

december

12 MONDAY

Our Lady of Guadalupe Day (MEX)

13 TUESDAY

14 WEDNESDAY

15 THURSDAY

Full Moon ○

16 FRIDAY

17 SATURDAY

18 SUNDAY

Brush Dance

december

JANUARY 2017

s	m	t	w	t	f	s
1	2	3	4	5	6	7
8	9	10	11	12	13	14
15	16	17	18	19	20	21
22	23	24	25	26	27	28
29	30	31				

MONDAY 19

TUESDAY 20

WEDNESDAY 21

THURSDAY 22

Winter Solstice - Winter begins
Last Quarter Moon ☽

FRIDAY 23

SATURDAY 24

Christmas Eve

SUNDAY 25

Brush Dance

Hanukkah
Christmas

DECEMBER

s	m	t	w	t	f	s
				1	2	3
4	5	6	7	8	9	10
11	12	13	14	15	16	17
18	19	20	21	22	23	24
25	26	27	28	29	30	31

december

26 MONDAY

27 TUESDAY

Kwanzaa begins
St. Stephen's Day (IRE)
Boxing Day (AUS, CAN, NZ, & UK)

28 WEDNESDAY

29 THURSDAY

New Moon ●

30 FRIDAY

31 SATURDAY

New Year's Eve

Notes

Brush Dance

Notes

Notes

Notes

shining through

How often do you fall into the silly habit of catching yourself being unworthy or foolish?

What if you were to suddenly shift from foolish to fearless? Yes, you can do this! Easy as pride.

You can catch yourself flourishing, flowering and flowing, being free.

You can catch your fearless spirit shining through.

Notes

Notes

Notes

Notes

Notes

Notes

Notes

Notes

Notes

Notes

Notes

Notes